Hidden
in the Jungle

AN ANTI-STRESS COLOURING BOOK WITH 60 ILLUSTRATIONS

S A R A   M U Z I O

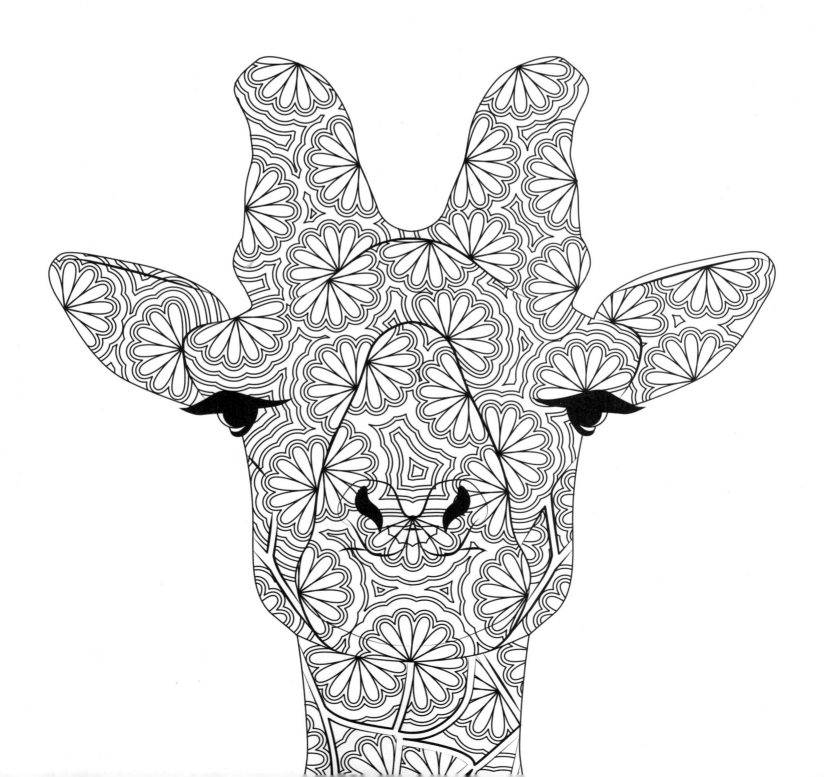

SARA MUZIO

Sara Muzio has over ten years of experience working in graphic design and illustration. In 2002, after earning a degree in Medical Illustration, she began working for small graphic design studios and in 2004 she became the scientific illustrator for Lumen Edizioni, where she completed a postgraduate course on publishing and advertising graphics. From 2005 to 2011, Sara worked as a freelance graphic designer for private clients as well as public entities and publishing houses. From 2011 to 2013, she was the graphic and packaging designer for Sambonet Paderno Industrie S.p.A. She currently works as an illustrator and freelance graphic designer. In addition to the illustrations found in this book, she created those for *Flower Fantasy – An Anti-stress Colouring Book with 60 Illustrations*, *The Extraordinary Journey of a Little Goldfish – Anti-stress Colouring Book*, *A Fantastic Journey along Swallow Migratory Routes – Anti-stress Colouring Book* and *Zen Garden – An Anti-stress Colouring Book with 60 Illustrations* for White Star Publishers.

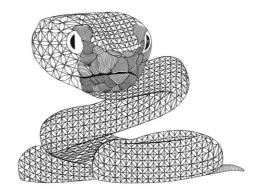

COVER GRAPHIC DESIGN
Michela Barbonaglia

GRAPHIC LAYOUT
Valentina Giammarinaro

WHITE STAR PUBLISHERS

WS White Star Publishers® is a registered trademark property of De Agostini Libri S.p.A.

© 2015 De Agostini Libri S.p.A.
Via G. da Verrazano, 15
28100 Novara, Italy
www.whitestar.it - www.deagostini.it

Translation: ICEIGEO, Milan

ISBN 978-88-544-1003-9

2 3 4 5 6   20 19 18 17 16

Printed in China

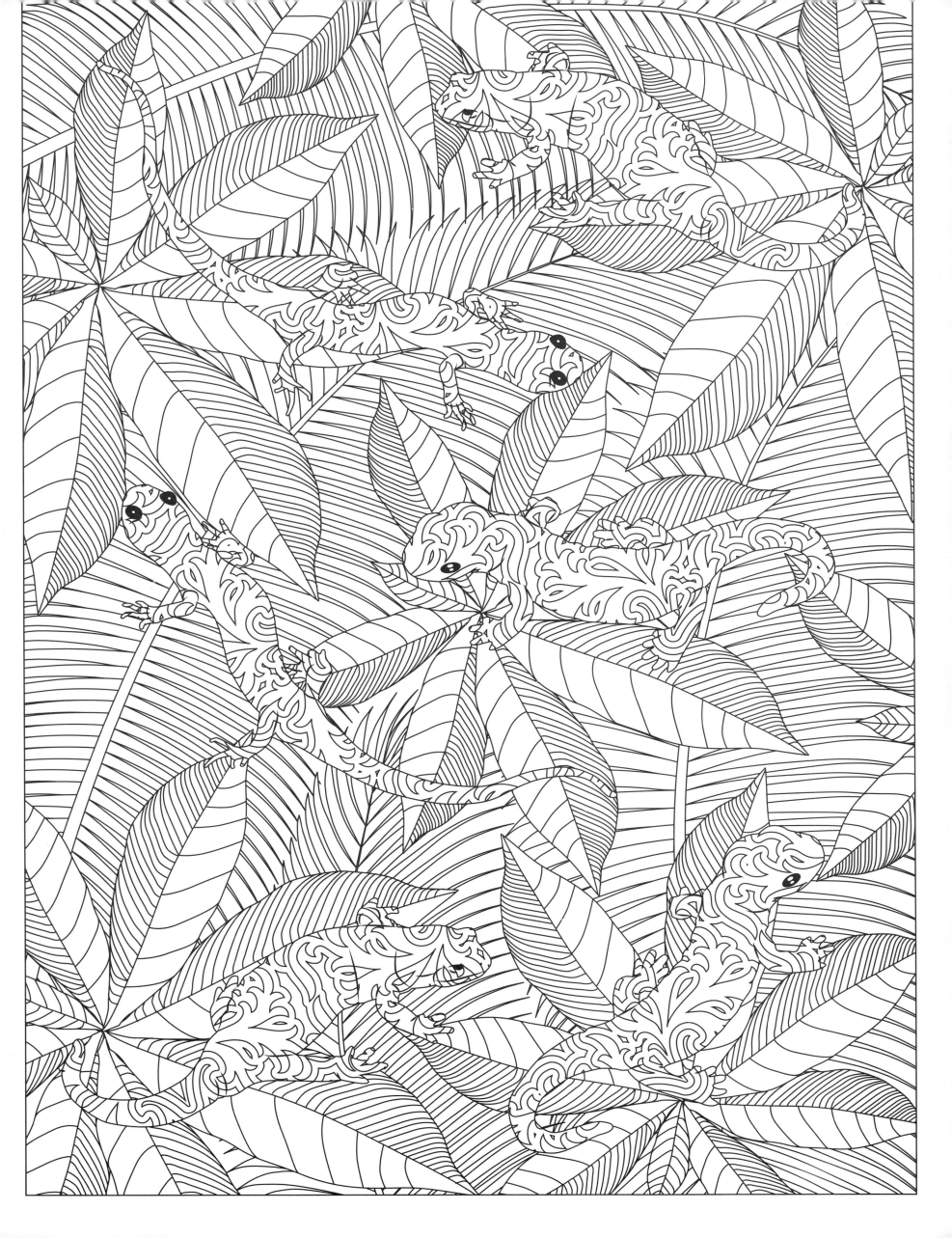

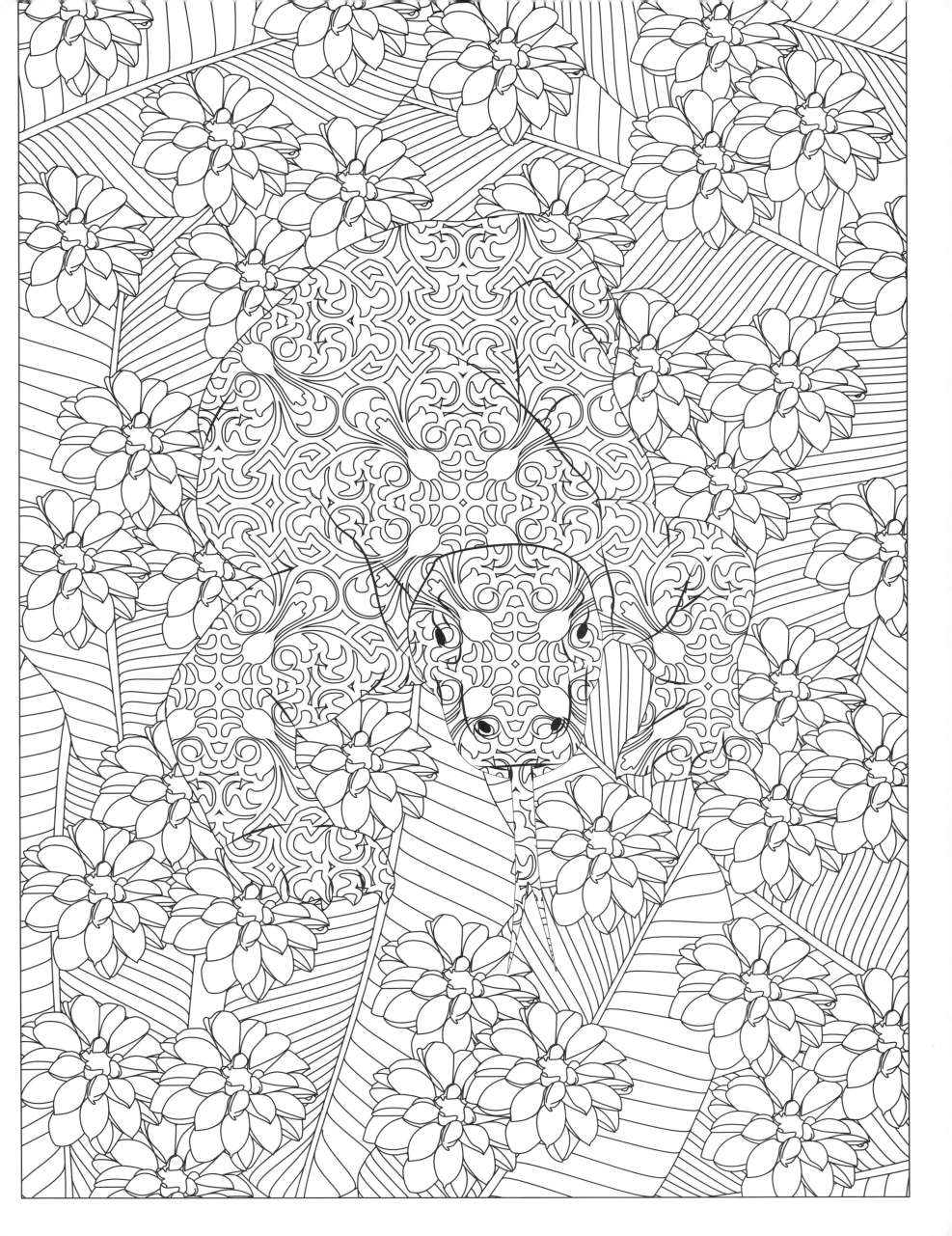

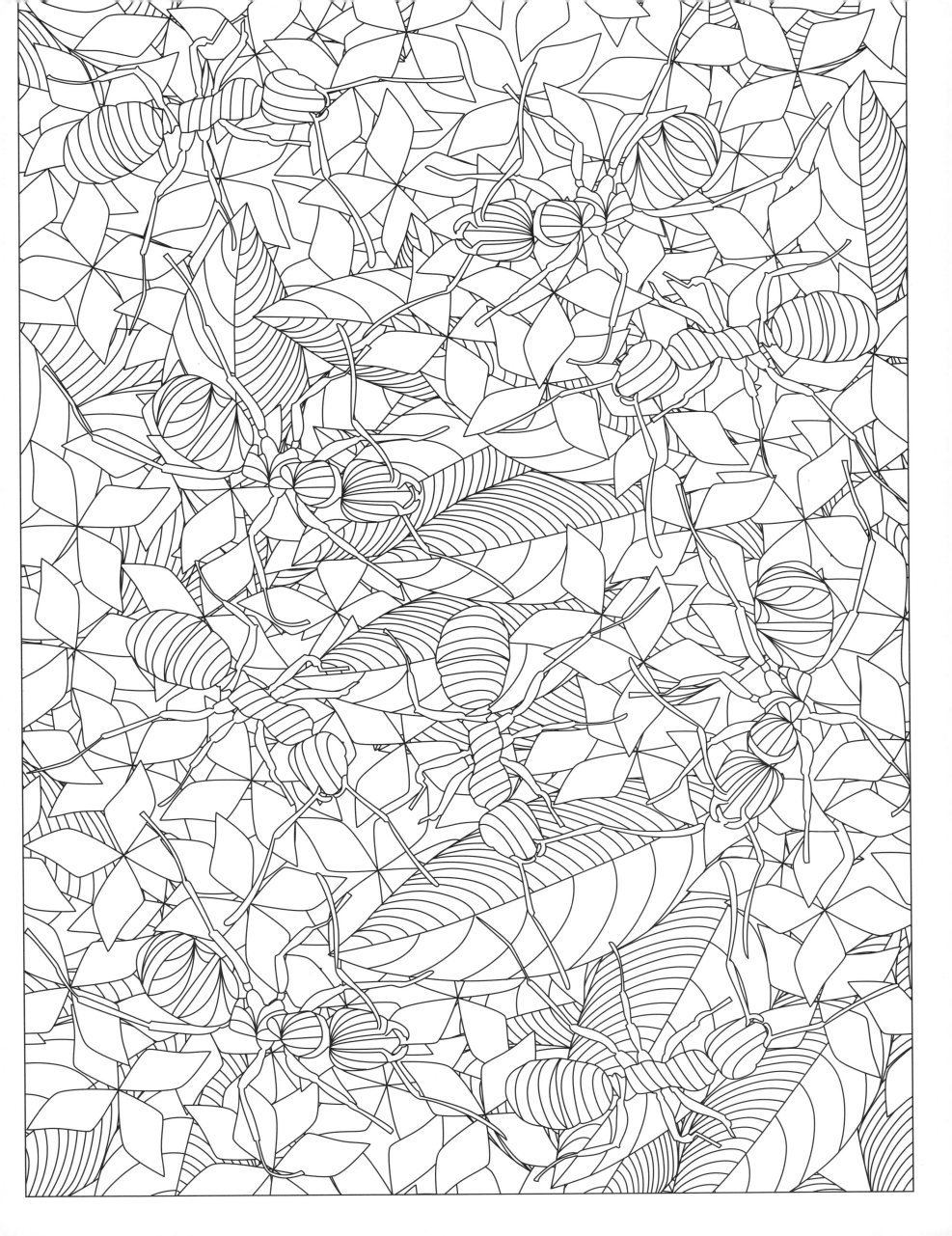

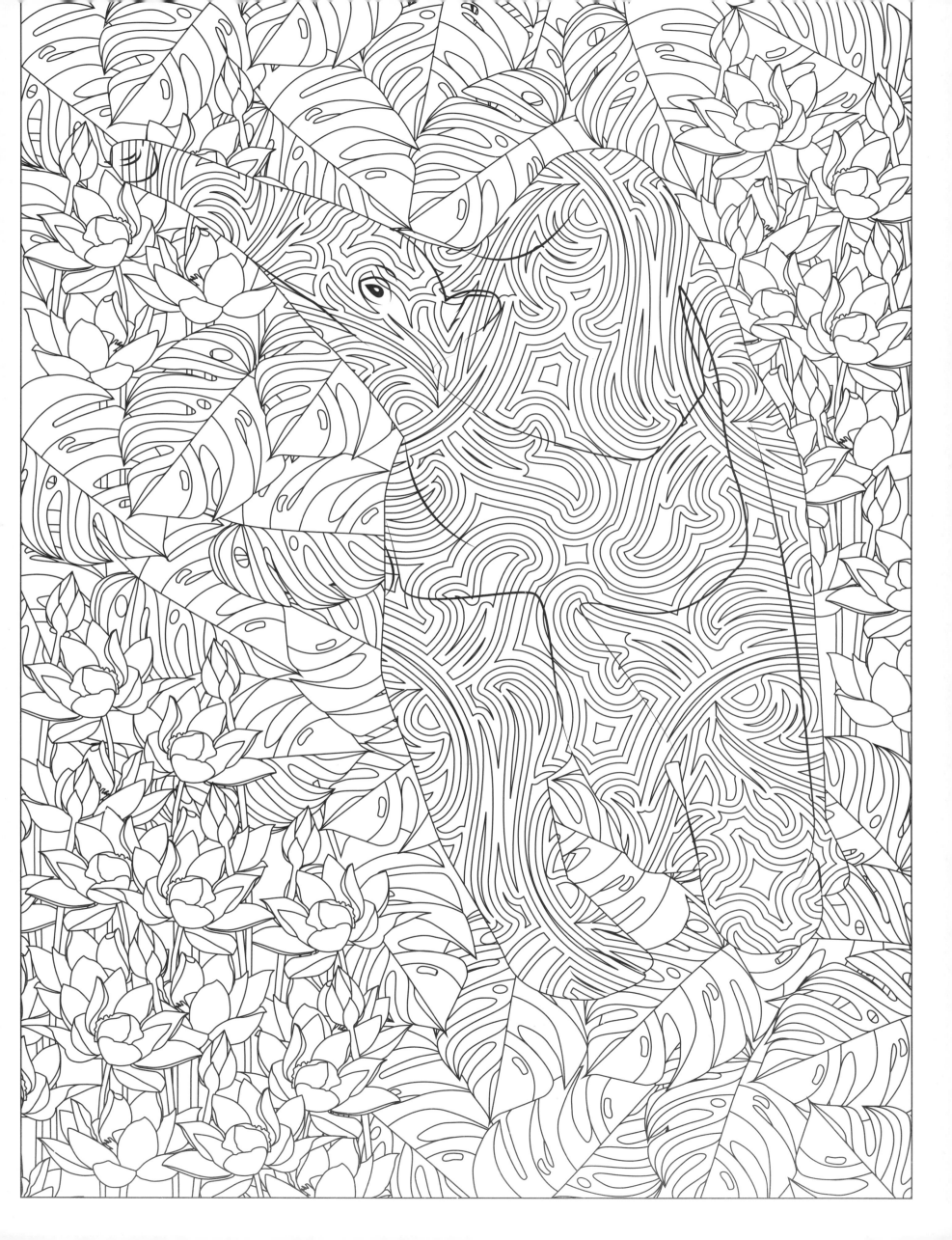

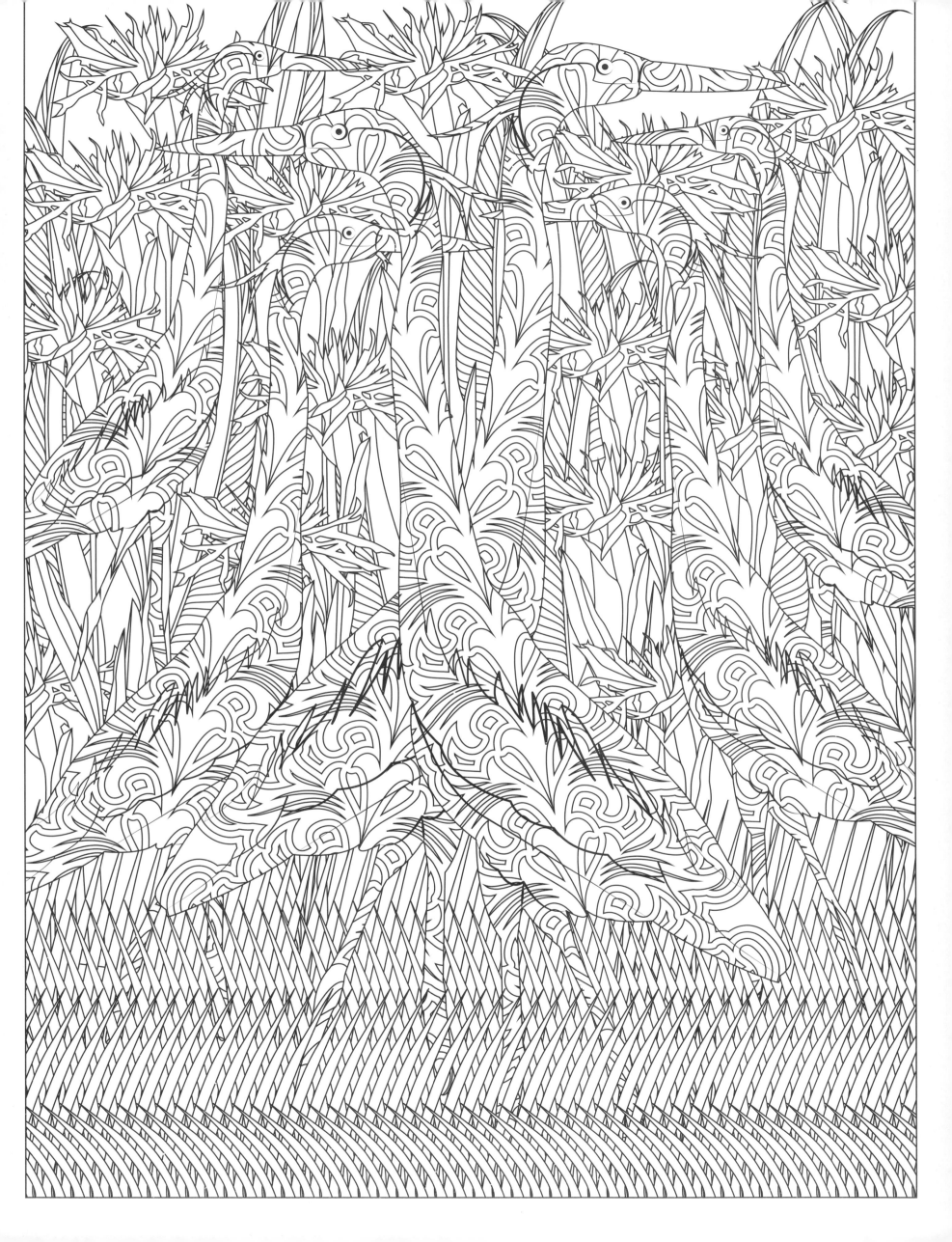

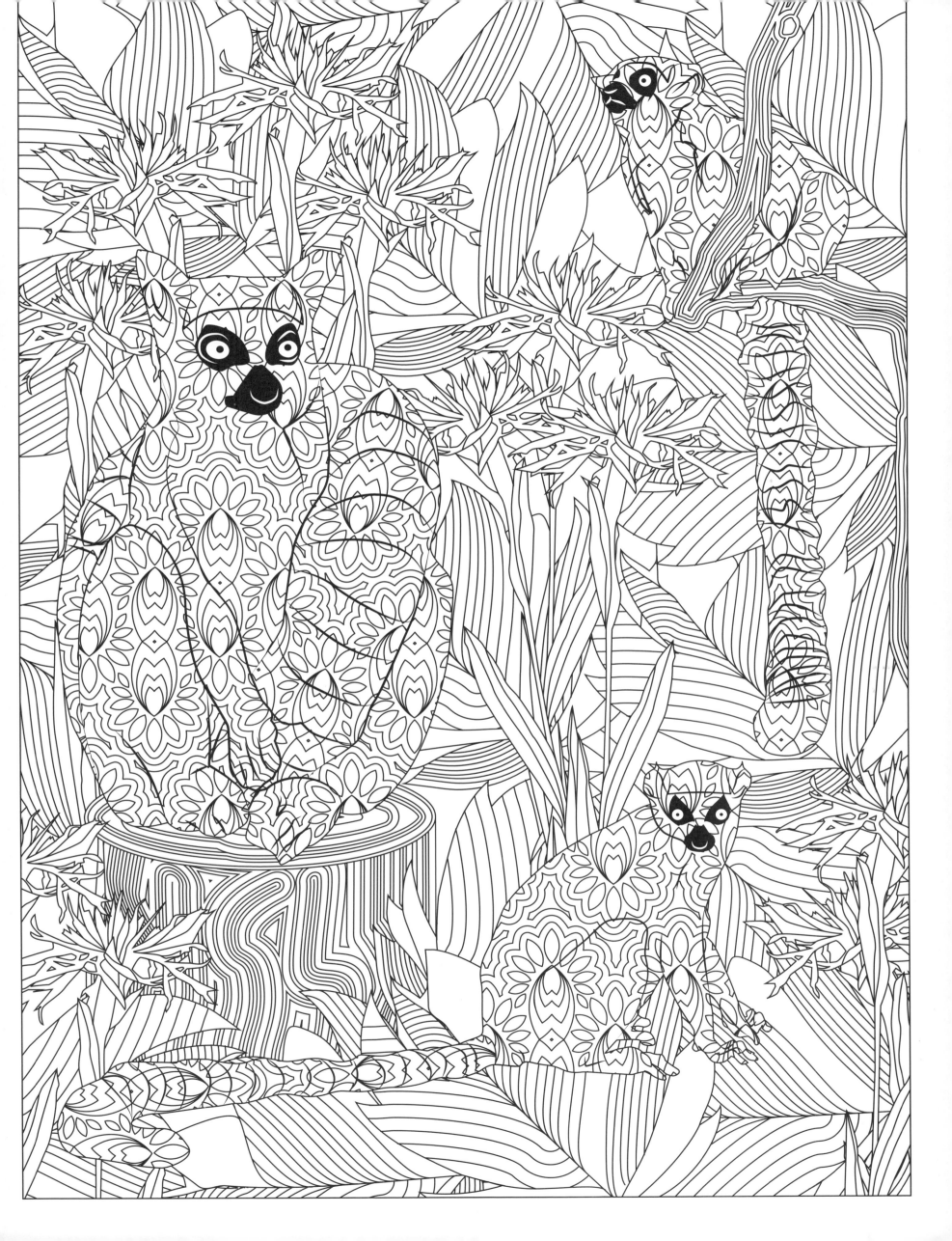

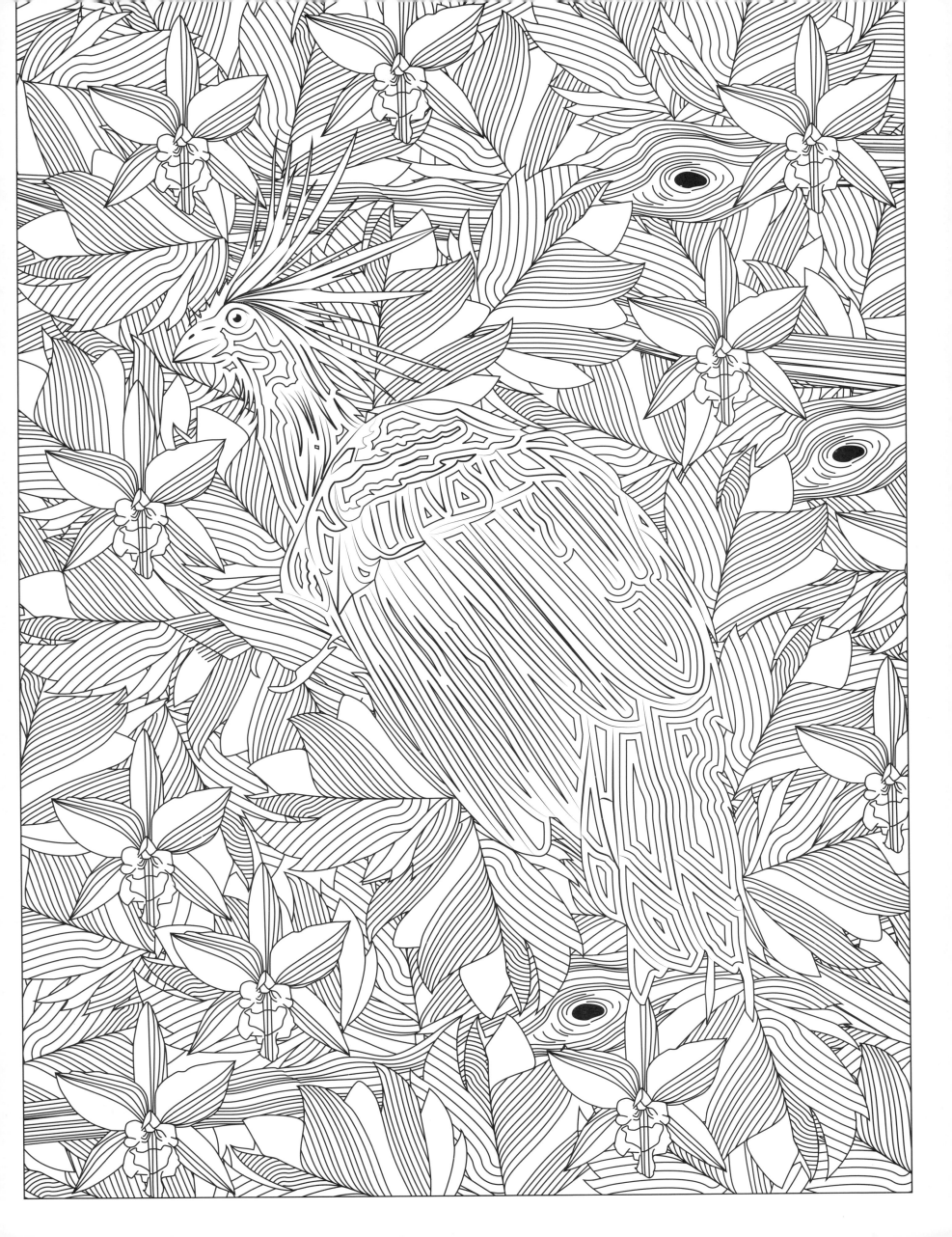

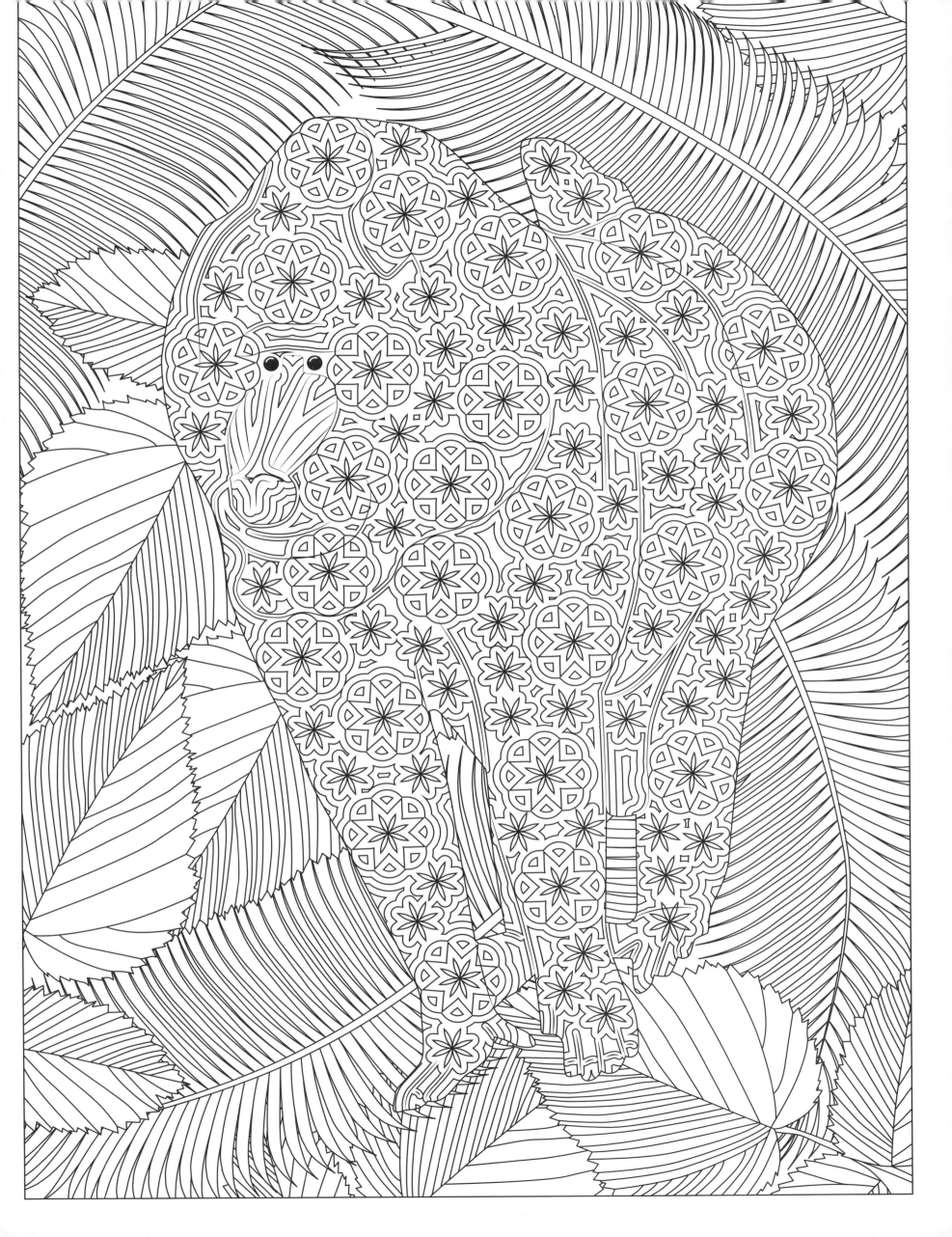

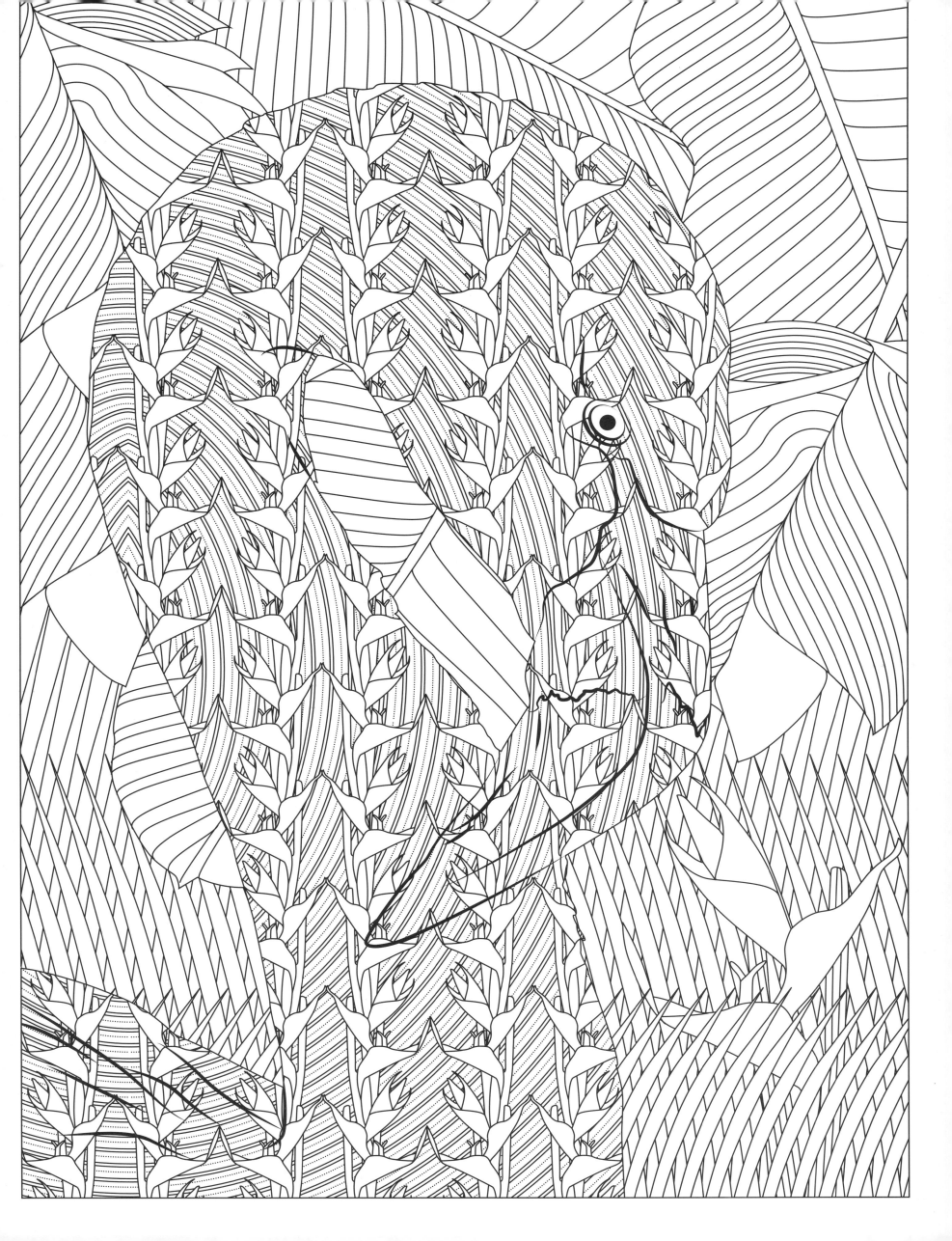

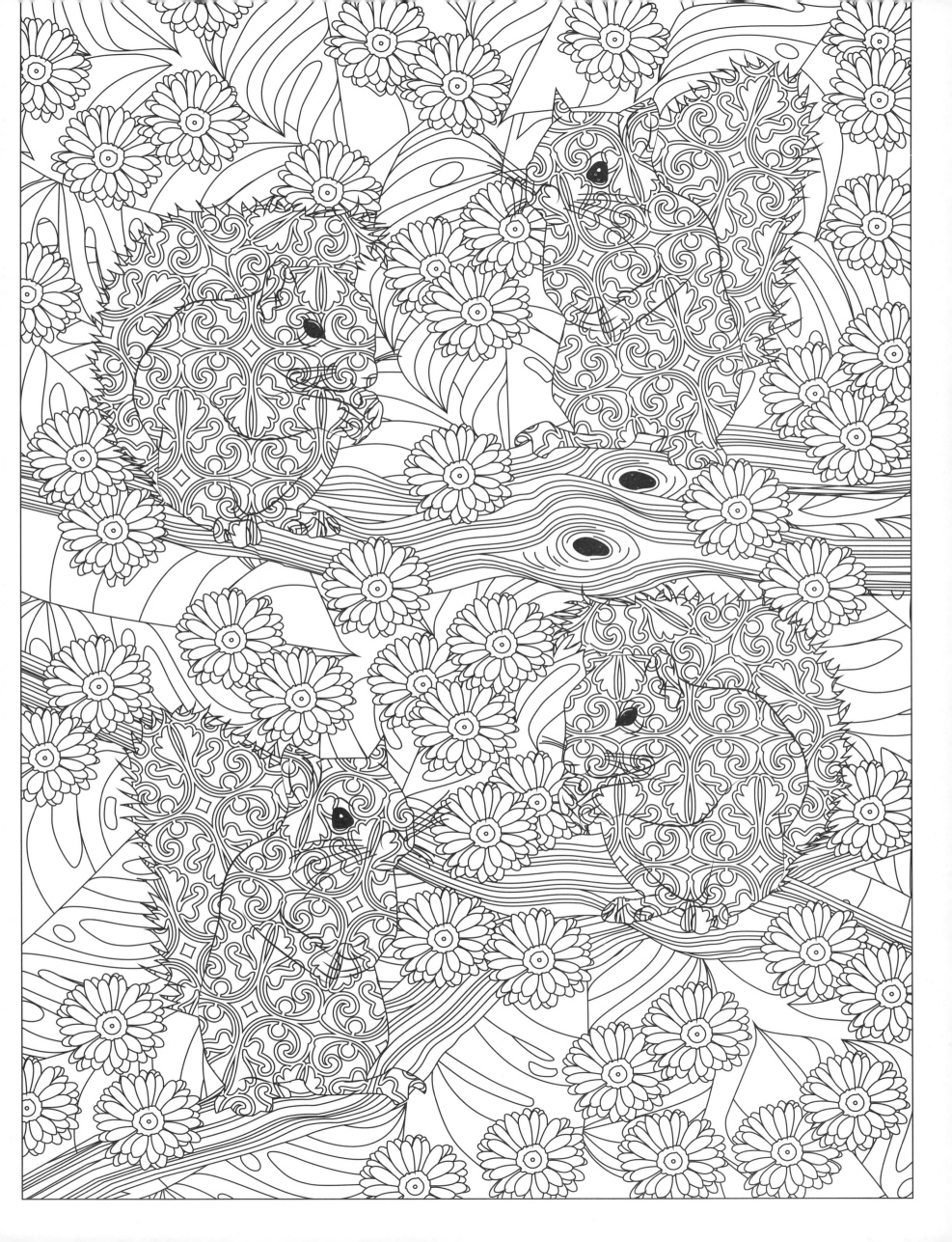

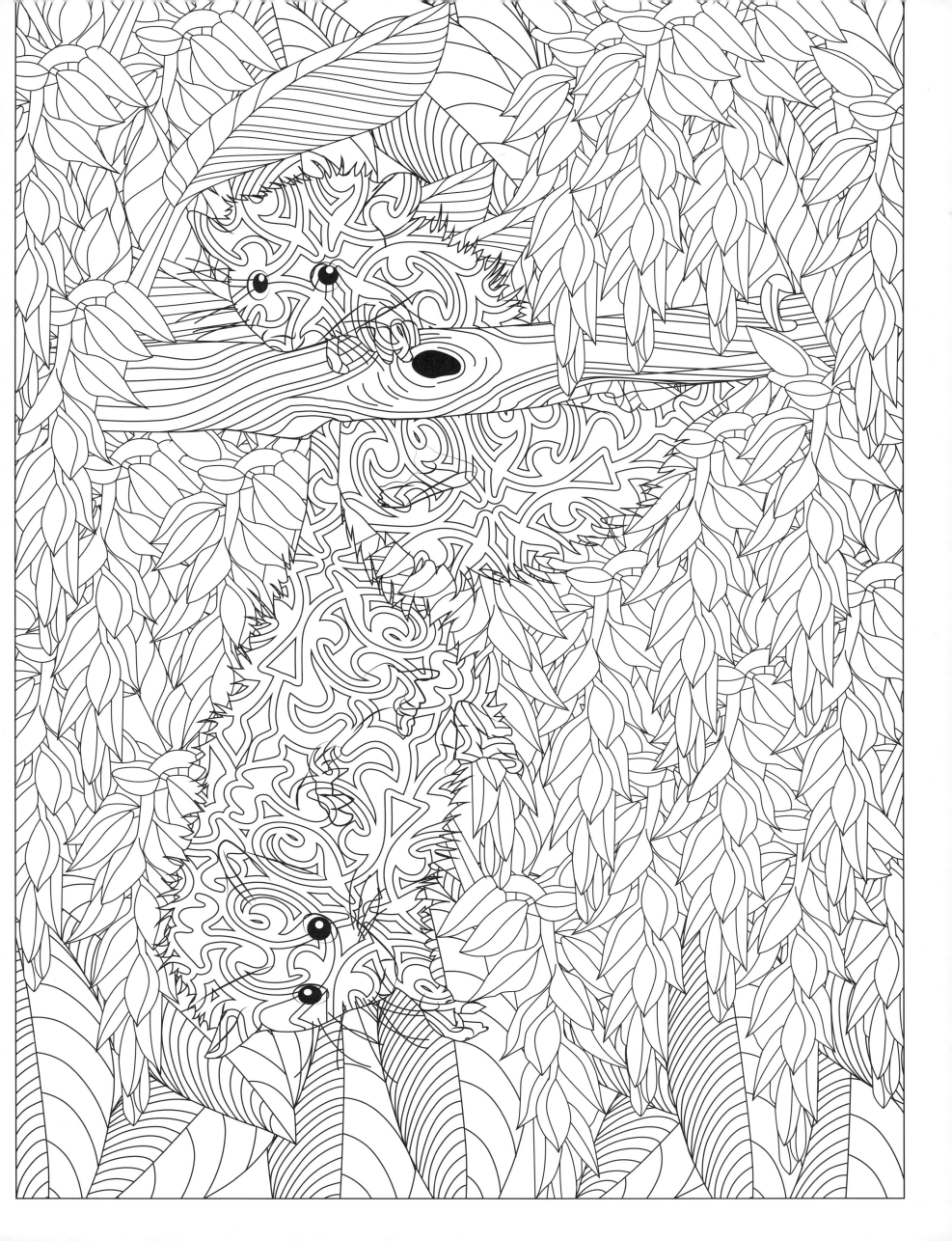

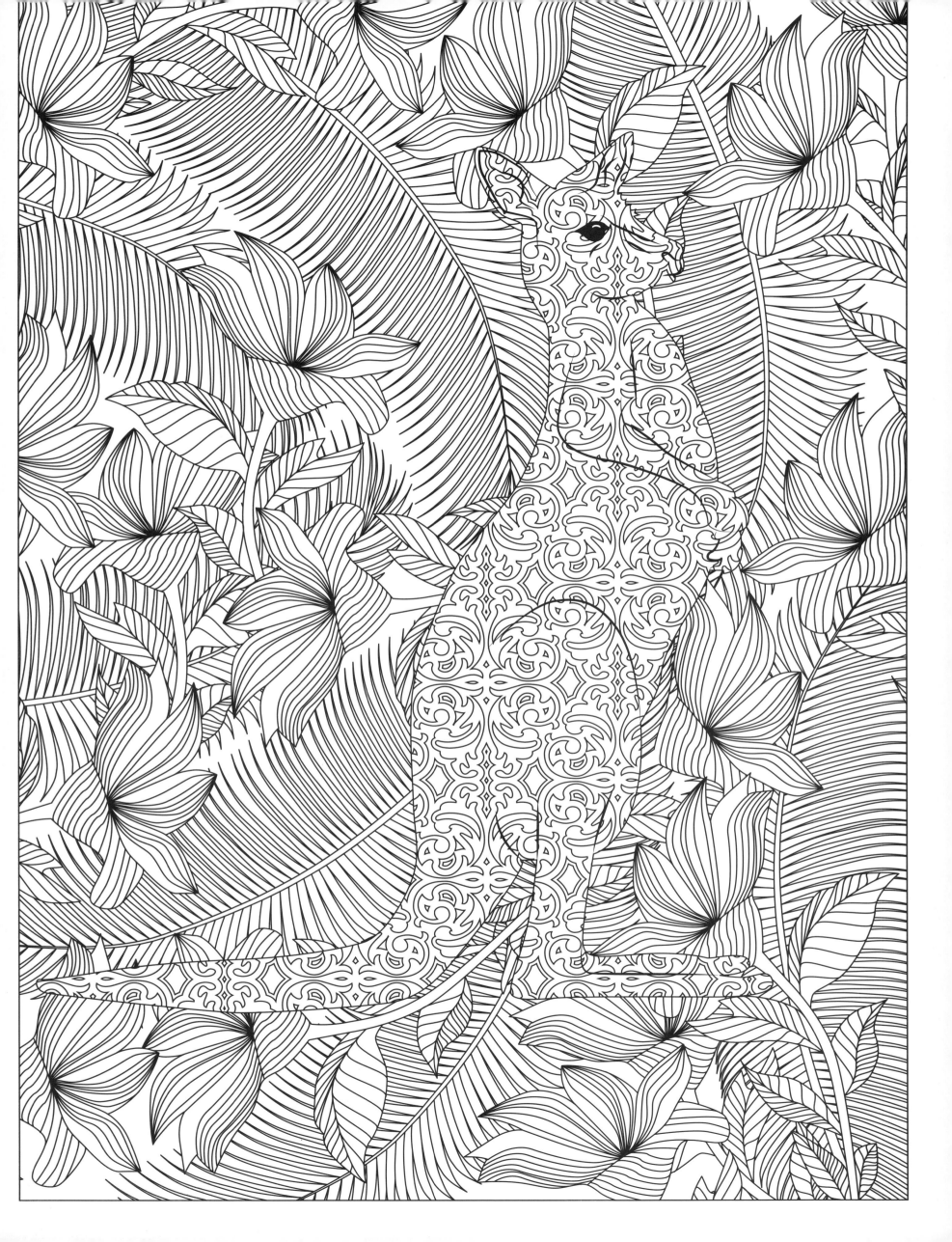

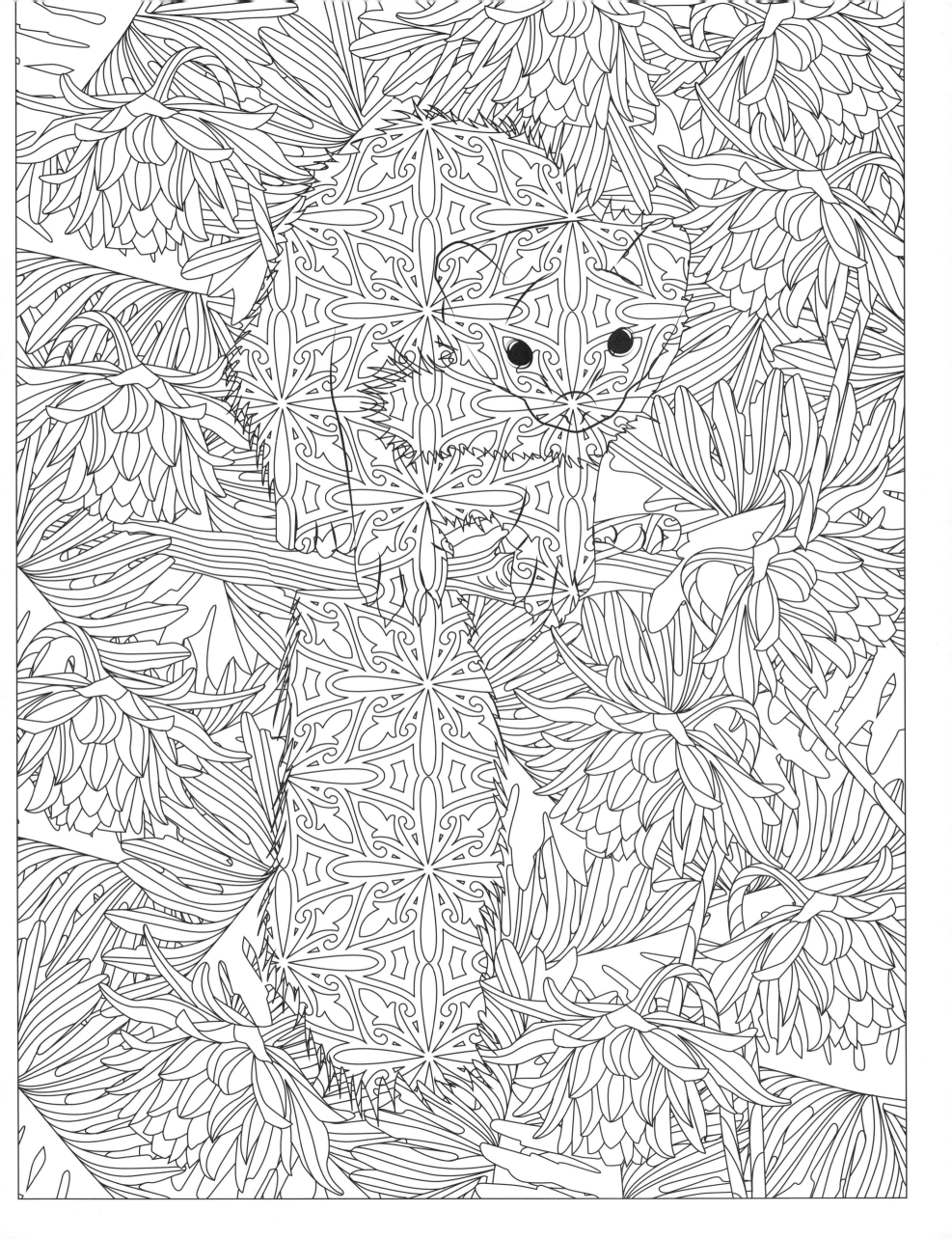

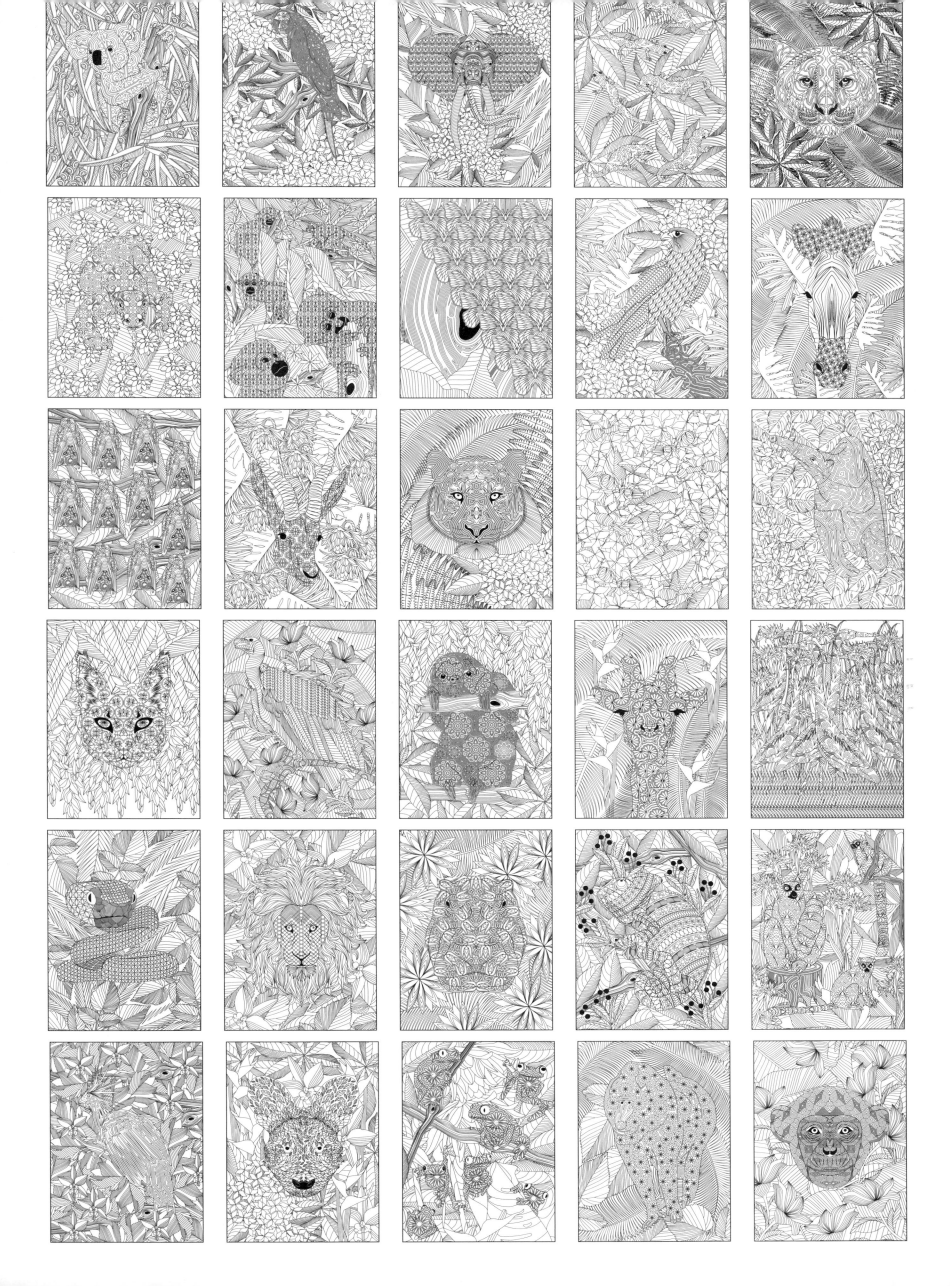

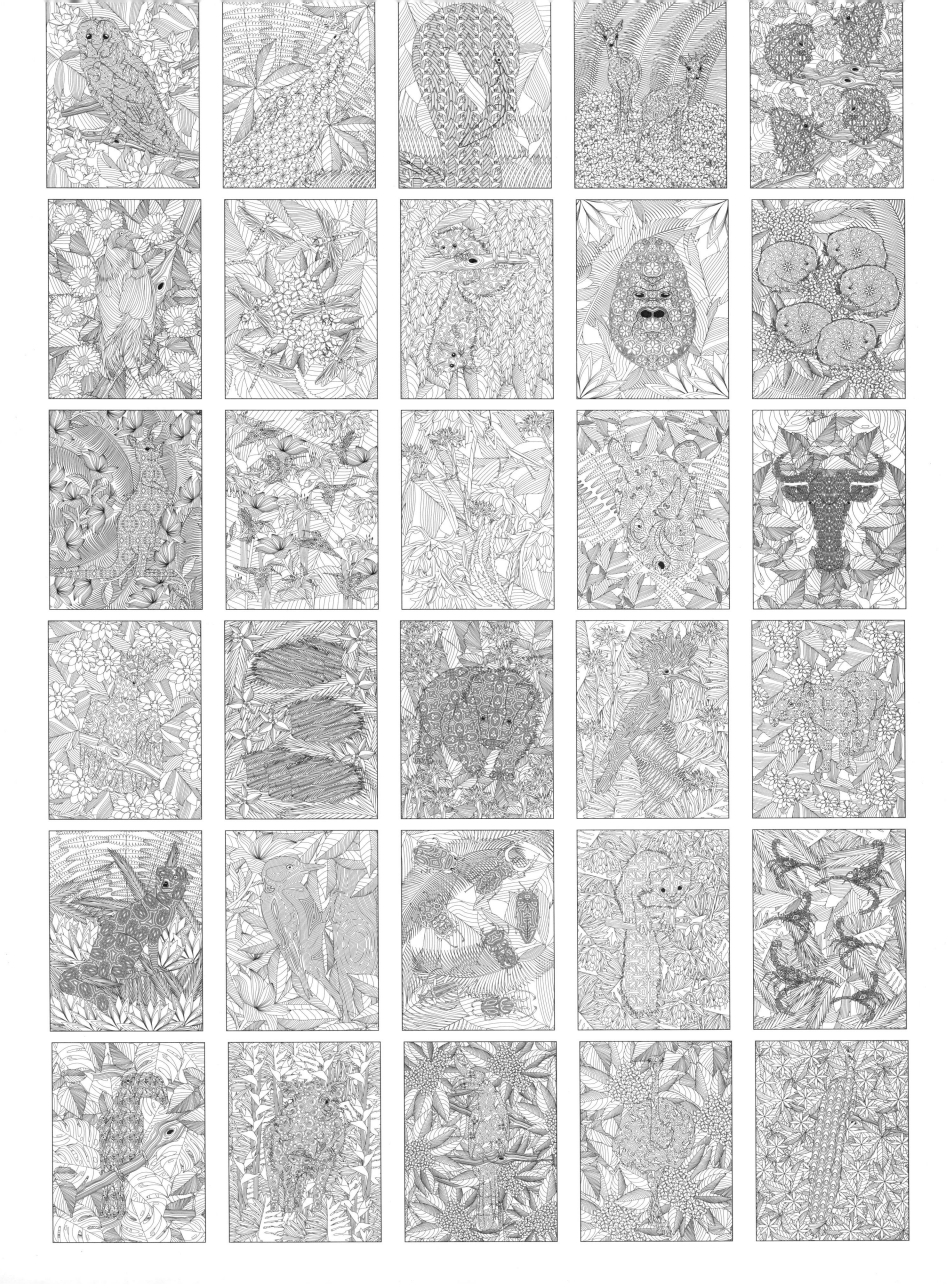